Mathematics
WORKBOOK

Author **Paul Broadbent**

KS2

VISUAL
REVISION
GUIDE

SUCCESS

CONTENTS

Numbers are made from the ten <u>digits</u>:

| 0 | 1 | 2 | 3 | 4 | 5 | 6 | 7 | 8 | 9 |

Remember that the position of a digit in a number gives its value.

$$2375 = 2000 + 300 + 70 + 5$$

thousands hundreds tens ones

To multiply by 10 move each digit one place to the left.

The empty place is filled by a zero.

145 × 10

1450

To divide by 10 move each digit one place to the right.

740 ÷ 10

74

VEXING PLACE VALUES

Q1 **Write these as numbers.**

a three thousand two hundred and six _____

b five thousand seven hundred and forty-one _____

c eight thousand one hundred and ninety _____

d nine thousand nine hundred and nineteen _____

e four thousand and fifty-two _____

f seven thousand six hundred and eleven _____

Q2 Write the missing numbers.

a 4152 = 4000 + [ ] + 50 + [ ]

b 7338 = [ ] + 300 + [ ] + 8

c 9624 = [ ] + [ ] + [ ] + [ ]

d 8513 = [ ] + [ ] + [ ] + [ ]

e 2299 = [ ] + [ ] + [ ] + [ ]

f 1687 = [ ] + [ ] + [ ] + [ ]

Q3 Multiply each number by 10 and 100. Write the answers.

a 34 x 10 → [ ]
       x100 → [ ]

b 70 x 10 → [ ]
       x100 → [ ]

c 56 x 10 → [ ]
       x100 → [ ]

d 92 x 10 → [ ]
       x100 → [ ]

KEY DATA

Multiplying and dividing by 10 moves the digits one place. Multiplying and dividing by 100 moves the digits two places. Look at these.

| | | 3 | 8 | x 1 0 0 =
| 3 | 8 | 0 | 0 |

| 4 | 2 | 0 | 0 | ÷ 1 0 0 =
| | | 4 | 2 |

Hi, I'm Sam!

This is a good game to play on your own or with a friend. If you're unlucky you may have to play it with a bossy sister like Mel! Use digit cards 0-9 shuffled and placed face down.

Draw four boxes and turn over the top card. Write the digit in one of the boxes. Once you have written the digit, have three more goes until the 4-digit number is complete. You are trying to make the largest 4-digit number possible. Check your number. Is it the largest number possible, or at least a larger number than your friends? Play 5 times and see who wins the most.

Challenge

BRAIN TEASER

Follow and complete these number trails.

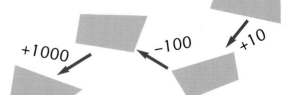

4825 +100 → 4925 −1000

+1000   −100   +10

ORDER! ORDER!

When you need to work out the order of numbers, try writing them under each other. Remember to line up the ones.

For example, let's put these in order starting with the smallest.

3847   4033   3800   435   3478

Line them up and put them in order.

thousands	hundreds	tens	ones
	4	3	5
3	4	7	8
3	8	0	0
3	8	4	7
4	0	3	3

We use < and > to compare numbers.

< means is less than	> means is greater than
For example 382 < 391	For example 880 > 808
382 is less than 391	880 is greater than 808

Q1 Write these numbers in order, starting with the smallest.

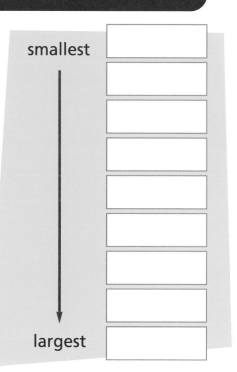

715
5771
705
517
7005
5775
75
570
5110

smallest

largest

Q2 Write the signs > or < for each pair of numbers.

a 58 ☐ 85

b 640 ☐ 604

c 372 ☐ 723

d 1090 ☐ 1900

e 4782 ☐ 2487

f 165 ☐ 156

g 9300 ☐ 9033

h 4114 ☐ 4111

i 2978 ☐ 5240

j 621 ☐ 612

k 9801 ☐ 9810

l 898 ☐ 889

Q3 These numbers are in order. Circle the two numbers that have swapped places in each of these.

a 56   57   61   59   60   58

b 3131   3133   3132   3134   3135   3136

c 988   989   990   993   992   991

d 420   410   430   440   450   460

e 6400   6500   6700   6600   6800   6900

KEY DATA

Remember to read each number from the left to the right. Compare all the thousands first and put them in order, then the hundreds, then the tens, and finally the ones.

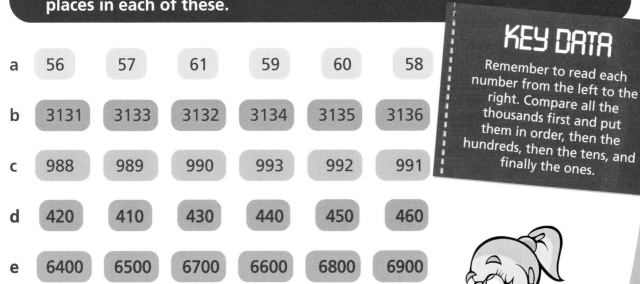

I'm Mel! For this tricky challenge you need a set of digit cards 1–9. The tricky bit for me is finding the cards in Sam's messy room! Choose any four cards and use them to make as many 4-digit numbers as you can. Write them in order, starting with the smallest. How many different 4-digit numbers can you make? Try it again with different sets of digits. Oh no, I've got to search Sam's room again to find 4 more!

Challenge

BRAIN TEASER

Write numbers that could go in the boxes.

1 38 > ☐ < ☐ > ☐ > 51

2 127 < ☐ > ☐ > ☐ < 131

Rounding makes numbers easier to work with. It means changing them to the nearest ten or hundred. This is very useful when you need to estimate a rough answer for a calculation.

Rounding to the nearest 10

Look at the ones digit.

If it is 5 or more, round up the tens digit.

If it is less than 5, the tens digit stays the same.

415 rounds up to 420

634 rounds down to 630

Rounding to the nearest 100

Look at the tens digit.

If it is 5 or more, round up the hundreds digit.

If it is less than 5, the hundreds digit stays the same.

463 rounds up to 500

836 rounds down to 800

Use rounding to work out approximate answers:

489 + 307 is approximately 500 + 300 = 800

47 × 4 is approximately 50 × 4 = 200

REMARKABLE ROUNDING

Q1 Round these numbers to the nearest 10 and 100.

		Nearest 10	Nearest 100
a	124		
b	402		
c	578		
d	315		
e	653		
f	245		

Q2 Round these amounts to the nearest pound.

a £1.38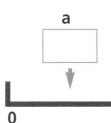

c £7.19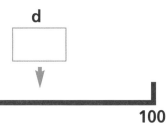

b £4.61

d £8.50

Q3 Estimate which number each arrow points to.

a	b	c		d

0 — 100

Q4 Round these to the nearest 10 to give approximate answers.

a 315 + 26 =

b 22 × 38 =

c 697 − 403 =

d 94 + 75 =

KEY DATA
We round up if the number is halfway between two tens or two hundreds. So, for example, 265 rounds up to 270 and 850 rounds up to 900.

Play the game 'More or less' with a partner. Choose someone who doesn't cheat ... not like Sam!

Your partner puts a calculation into a calculator, such as 18x39, and hides the answer (702) from you. You then estimate the answer and say whether it is more or less than the real answer. So if you estimate that the answer is 'less than 800', you are correct and win a point (hurrah!).

If you are incorrect your partner wins a point (boo!). See who is first to reach 5 points.

I hope I get more, not less than Sam!

Challenge

BRAIN TEASER

Join each of these shopping bills to their best approximate answer.

1		2		3	
	45p		83p		65p
	27p		78p		97p
	93p		39p		13p
	61p		17p		21p
	£2.20		£2.00		£2.30

SUPER SEQUENCES AND PATTERNS

A number sequence is a list of numbers in a pattern.
Sequences can go up:

| 9 | 13 | 17 | 21 | 350 | 400 | 450 | 500 |

or down...

| 420 | 400 | 380 | 360 | 57 | 55 | 53 | 51 |

To find the rule or pattern in a sequence look at the
differences between each number.

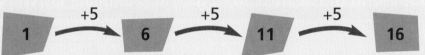

| 1 | +5 → | 6 | +5 → | 11 | +5 → | 16 |

The rule or pattern is +5

| 130 | −10 → | 120 | −10 → | 110 | −10 → | 100 |

The rule or pattern is −10

Q1 Write the next three numbers in each of these sequences.

a 4   10   16   22   ☐ ☐ ☐

b 38   33   28   23   ☐ ☐ ☐

c 370   390   410   430   ☐ ☐ ☐

d 625   600   575   550   ☐ ☐ ☐

e 307   305   303   301   ☐ ☐ ☐

Q2 Write the missing numbers in each of these sequences.

a　14　17　☐　23　☐　29　32

b　700　☐　600　550　☐　450　400

c　12　16　☐　24　☐　32　36

d　☐　49　42　35　28　☐　14

Q3 Write the missing numbers on these number tracks.

a　| −8 | −6 | | −2 | | | |

b　| | | −7 | −5 | −3 | | |

c　| | −10 | −5 | | | | 15 |

d　| 25 | 15 | | | −15 | | |

KEY DATA

Some sequences go back past zero into negative numbers. When you count on or back with negative numbers it is really helpful to picture a number line.

−5 −4 −3 −2 −1 0 1 2 3 4 5

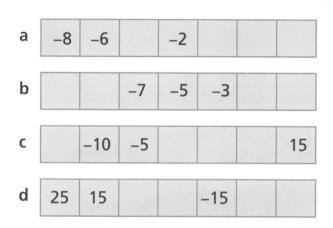

I like playing Number Pattern Detectives. Try this game yourself with a set of digit cards 2–9. Choose any two numbers up to 98 as your start number. Then shuffle the leftover cards and choose the top card. This shows the step size for your sequence, counting backwards. You need to think hard and predict whether zero will be in your sequence.

For example, if you choose 63 as your start number and 9 is the top card, you take away 9 each time and so zero will be part of the sequence.

63　54　45　36　27　18　9　0

See how good you are at predicting number patterns that end in zero.

Challenge

BRAIN TEASER

Numbers are missing from this 100-square. Try to work out the pattern and write in the missing numbers.

	11				16		
		45			49		
		70			74		21
			89				
6							
	39					56	
3							
					60		
1					30		

A fraction has two numbers, one below and one above the line. The bottom number of the fraction tells you the number of equal parts. The top number of the fraction tells you how many parts are taken.

1 part out of 5 taken. This shows $\frac{1}{5}$.

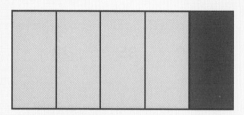

3 parts out of 5 taken. This shows $\frac{3}{5}$.

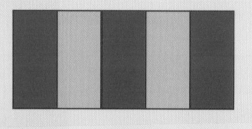

FANTASTIC FRACTIONS

Q1 Write the fraction that each shape is shaded in red. Some of them look different, but turn out to be the same!

a _____

b _____

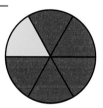

c _____

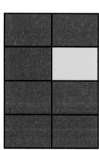

d _____

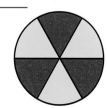

e _____

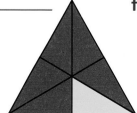

f _____

Q2 Colour these shapes to show the fractions.

a $\frac{1}{7}$

b $\frac{2}{3}$

c $\frac{5}{8}$

Q3 Join together all the shapes that have the same equivalent fractions shaded.

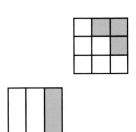

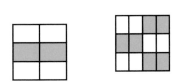

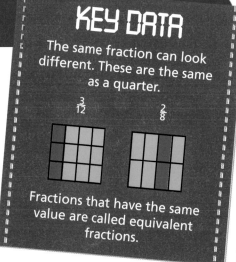

KEY DATA

The same fraction can look different. These are the same as a quarter.

$\frac{3}{12}$ $\frac{2}{8}$

Fractions that have the same value are called equivalent fractions.

This puzzle was too tricky for Mel, as she only has a fraction of my brains! You have a go - I found it easy!

How many different ways can you colour half of this square? You must colour whole triangles.

Challenge

BRAIN TEASER

Write these fractions in order starting with the smallest. If there are any you are unsure of, make them equivalent to another fraction and compare them.

$\frac{3}{5}$ $\frac{1}{2}$ $\frac{7}{10}$ $\frac{4}{5}$ $\frac{1}{4}$ $\frac{3}{4}$

___ ___ ___ ___ ___ ___

Working out fractions of amounts is the same as dividing.

To find fractions of amounts, just divide by the denominator.

Look at these:

Finding one half is the same as dividing by 2.

$\frac{1}{2}$ of 14

is the same as

$14 \div 2$

which is 7.

Finding one quarter is the same as dividing by 4.

$\frac{1}{4}$ of 12

is the same as

$12 \div 4$

which is 3.

FUNNY FRACTIONS OF AMOUNTS

Q1 Answer these.

a $\frac{1}{2}$ of 16 = ☐

b $\frac{1}{4}$ of 20 = ☐

c $\frac{1}{10}$ of 30 = ☐

d $\frac{1}{2}$ of 22 = ☐

e $\frac{1}{3}$ of 21 = ☐

f $\frac{1}{4}$ of 16 = ☐

g $\frac{1}{5}$ of 15 = ☐

h $\frac{1}{6}$ of 12 = ☐

i $\frac{1}{7}$ of 21 = ☐

j $\frac{1}{11}$ of 44 = ☐

Q2 Here are some fractions of 24. What amount is each?

a $\frac{1}{4}$ = [ ]

b $\frac{1}{3}$ = [ ]

24

c $\frac{1}{2}$ = [ ]

d $\frac{1}{6}$ = [ ]

Q3 Write the answers to these word problems.

a What is half of £1.20? _____

b A tray holds 12 eggs.
A quarter of the eggs are
broken. How many eggs are broken? _____

c Jade has 18 sweets. She gives a
third to her friend. How many
sweets does she give her friend? _____

d There are 30 children in class. A tenth of the
children are away. How many children are away? _____

e A cake is sliced into 8 pieces. Four slices are eaten.
What fraction of the cake is left? _____

KEY DATA

Look at this question:

What fraction of 1 metre
is 25cm?

With questions that ask for
fractions of amounts like this,
use division to work it out.
How many lots of 25cm are
there in 1 metre? There are 4,
so 25cm is $\frac{1}{4}$ of 1 metre.

Challenge

Use a handful of coins
or buttons for this challenge.
If you have a sister like mine, use
buttons, because she will spend the
coins in no time!

Take a handful of the buttons and count
them. For example, you may scoop up 18 buttons.
You need to work out how many different ways
you can group them to make a fraction of 18:

$\frac{1}{2}$ of 18 = 9

$\frac{1}{3}$ of 18 = 6

$\frac{1}{6}$ of 18 = 3

$\frac{1}{9}$ of 18 = 2

Try it with different
amounts.

BRAIN TEASER

Look at each of these. What fraction
of the larger bag is the smaller bag?

1 _____

2 _____

3 _____

MENTAL ADDITION MAYHEM

When you need to add numbers in your head, look at the numbers and work out the best method. There are lots of methods. Try these ways of adding 39 + 57:

30 + 50 = 80

9 + 7 = 16

80 + 16 = 96

39 + 50 = 89

89 + 7 = 96

39 is 1 less than 40

40 + 57 = 97

97 − 1 = 96

Q1 Choose a mental method to answer each of these. You may use different methods for each question.

a 24 + 48 =

b 33 + 19 =

c 46 + 47 =

d 51 + 26 =

e 14 + 68 =

f 37 + 59 =

g 22 + 71 =

h 23 + 15 =

i 52 + 39 =

j 17 + 56 =

k 44 + 33 =

l 24 + 12 =

m 55 + 16 =

n 23 + 68 =

16

Q2 Join together numbers that total 75.

38
52
46
23
37
30
29
45

Q3 Write the cost of each of these.

KEY DATA

It is important to know all the addition facts to 20. Practise so that you can use them to help work out harder sums. For example, if you know 9 + 7 is 16, then you can quickly work these out:

90 + 70   900 + 700

19 + 17   109 + 107

a a bike and lights   £_____

b a toolkit and lock   £_____   e a toolkit and helmet £_____

c a helmet and lights   £_____   f two helmets   £_____

d a bike and lock   £_____   g two bikes   £_____

Challenge

I like messing around with digits. Have a go at this, with the digits 1 to 5.

Write down any 2-digit number with these digits, such as 45. Reverse the digits and write down that number → 54.

Add the two numbers together: 45+54 = 99.

Try the same thing with other reverse additions. What do you notice?

What if you use any digits from 1-9 to make the total go over 100?

Have a look for other patterns.

BRAIN TEASER

The outside numbers total the centre number. Write the missing numbers.

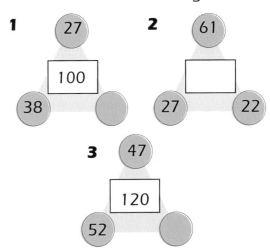

1   27
     100
38

2   61

27   22

3   47
     120
52

There are lots of different ways to take away one number from another.
Try these methods for 74 – 38.

> Count on from 38 to 40 and hold the 2 in your head.
>
> 74 – 40 is 34.
>
> 34 add 2 is 36.

> 74 – 38 is the same as 74 – 40 and then add 2
>
> 34 add 2 is 36

> 74 take away 30 is 44
>
> 44 take away 8 is 36

MENTAL SUBTRACTION MAYHEM

Q1 Choose a mental method to find the answers.

a 78 – 34 = ☐

b 52 – 19 = ☐

c 93 – 45 = ☐

d 31 – 16 = ☐

e 47 – 38 = ☐

f 64 – 27 = ☐

g 80 – 23 = ☐

h 75 – 58 = ☐

i 82 – 28 = ☐

j 63 – 51 = ☐

KEY DATA

Just like the addition facts, it is important to know all the subtraction facts to 20. Use them to help work out harder sums. For example, if you know 16 – 9 is 7, then you can quickly work these out:

160 – 90   1600 – 900

26 – 19   116 – 109

Q2 Choose a mental method to find the difference between these pairs of numbers.

a 62 81 → difference ☐   d 84 39 → difference ☐

b 56 95 → difference ☐   e 18 56 → difference ☐

c 43 25 → difference ☐   f 47 70 → difference ☐

Q3 These are the ages of the Green family. Answer these questions.

Gran 72   Mum 37   Dad 44   Ryan 18   Millie 15

a What is the age difference between Mum and Dad? _____

b How much older is Gran than Millie? _____

c How many years are there between Mum and Ryan? _____

d How much younger is Millie than Dad? _____

e How old was Dad when Ryan was born? _____

f Which two people have an age difference of 28 years? _____

g How many years is it until Gran is 100 years old? _____

I love doing word-searches! If only I could mentally subtract the word 'Sam!'

Make up your own 'Take away' word-search, with the answers written as words.

h	t	f	f
a	s	a	m
m	e	l	h
x	e	t	z

Challenge

BRAIN TEASER

Answer these questions using the five numbers.

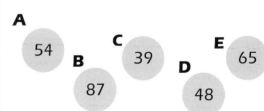

1 Which two numbers have a difference of 11? _____

2 What is B take away A? _____

3 Which letter is 26 less than E? _____

4 B − C = D. True or false? _____

WRITTEN ADDITION AND SUBTRACTION

When you need to add or subtract numbers, it is usually quicker to work out the answers in your head. But sometimes the numbers are just too big to hold in your head and this is when to use a written method.

Here are some examples of methods you could try. Do you use the same methods or have you got your own?

Addition

$$
\begin{array}{r}
328 \\
+ 64 \\
\hline
392 \\
1
\end{array}
$$

Write the 2 in the 'ones' <u>column</u> and put the ten under the 'tens' column.

Add the tens: 20, 60 and 10 and write 9 in the 'tens' column to show 90.

Write the 3 in the 'hundreds' column to make 392.

Subtraction

$$
\begin{array}{r}
3\overset{7}{8}4 \\
- 58 \\
\hline
326
\end{array}
$$

4 take away 8 can't be done, so change 84 into 70 and 14. 14 take away 8 is 6, so write this in the 'ones' column. 70 take away 50 is 20, so write 2 in the 'tens' column. Write the 3 in the 'hundreds' column to make 326.

Q1 Answer these additions.

a
$$
\begin{array}{r}
347 \\
+ 37 \\
\hline
\end{array}
$$

b
$$
\begin{array}{r}
264 \\
+ 53 \\
\hline
\end{array}
$$

c
$$
\begin{array}{r}
413 \\
+ 88 \\
\hline
\end{array}
$$

d
$$
\begin{array}{r}
276 \\
+ 315 \\
\hline
\end{array}
$$

Q2 Answer these subtractions.

a
$$
\begin{array}{r}
185 \\
- 47 \\
\hline
\end{array}
$$

b
$$
\begin{array}{r}
465 \\
- 82 \\
\hline
\end{array}
$$

c
$$
\begin{array}{r}
233 \\
- 64 \\
\hline
\end{array}
$$

d
$$
\begin{array}{r}
315 \\
- 144 \\
\hline
\end{array}
$$

Q3 Write the missing numbers.

a
```
  [ ] 8 [ ]
+     4 7
---------
  4   3 1
```

c
```
  [ ] 6 1
-     8 [ ]
---------
  6   7 3
```

b
```
  5 1 9
+   9 [ ]
-------
  6 [ ] 1
```

d
```
  6 [ ] 2
-     5 3
---------
  5   8 [ ]
```

Q4 Use written methods to answer these.

a 475 + 89 = [ ]

b 621 − 54 = [ ]

KEY DATA

If you use a 'vertical' written method for adding or taking away, make sure you line up the columns carefully. Ones should be above ones, tens above tens and hundreds above hundreds. Written addition and subtraction is easier if you start with the ones column and work your way left.

Challenge

Sam thinks he's clever. He can always work things out in his head. I prefer pen and paper. Which method do you prefer?

To find out, use a mental method and then a written method for 127+58 and 208−74.

Which was quickest? Are they similar methods?

Try to explain your methods to someone else.

Try the same thing with larger numbers – even Sam might have to use pen and paper for these.

BRAIN TEASER

Answer the first sum, then reverse one number in the first one to make the new answer. Here is an example to show you what to do.

```
   84      reverse      84
   26        26         62
 + 39      ----->      + 39
 -----                 -----
  149                   185
```

```
   31
   62
 + 24                 +
 -----               -----
                       81
```

Use this grid to help you learn the multiplication facts!

Circle any you don't know and try to learn them.

Remember – you can multiply in any order.

7 × 3 has the same answer as 3 × 7

Once you know your facts you can use them for trickier questions.

×	0	1	2	3	4	5	6	7	8	9	10
2	0	2	4	6	8	10	12	14	16	18	20
3	0	3	6	9	12	15	18	21	24	27	30
4	0	4	8	12	16	20	24	28	32	36	40
5	0	5	10	15	20	25	30	35	40	45	50
6	0	6	12	18	24	30	36	42	48	54	60
7	0	7	14	21	28	35	42	49	56	63	70
8	0	8	16	24	32	40	48	56	64	72	80
9	0	9	18	27	36	45	54	63	72	81	90
10	0	10	20	30	40	50	60	70	80	90	100

For example, if you know that 4 × 6 is 24, then 40 × 6 is ten times more: 240.

MESMERISING MULTIPLICATION

Q1 Answer these as quickly as you can. Time yourself to find your quickest time.

a $7 \times 2 =$

$4 \times 4 =$

$5 \times 9 =$

$3 \times 8 =$

$6 \times 6 =$

$4 \times 3 =$

$2 \times 10 =$

$5 \times 6 =$

b $8 \times 3 =$

$9 \times 2 =$

$5 \times 5 =$

$6 \times 7 =$

$10 \times 4 =$

$4 \times 9 =$

$3 \times 7 =$

$2 \times 8 =$

c $7 \times 9 =$

$5 \times 8 =$

$6 \times 3 =$

$4 \times 7 =$

$9 \times 8 =$

$5 \times 6 =$

$6 \times 8 =$

$9 \times 9 =$

Q2 Join pairs with the same product.

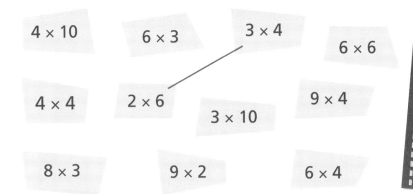

4 × 10   6 × 3   3 × 4   6 × 6

4 × 4   2 × 6   9 × 4

3 × 10

8 × 3   9 × 2   6 × 4

5 × 8   8 × 2   5 × 6

KEY DATA

To multiply a 2-digit number by a single digit, break the 2-digit number up.

34 × 6

1 Multiply the tens:
30 × 6 = 180

2 Multiply the ones: 6 × 4 = 24

3 Add the two parts:
180 + 24 = 204

Q3 Answer these.

a   3 × 5 =
     30 × 5 =

b   7 × 9 =
     70 × 9 =

c   8 × 4 =
     80 × 4 =

d   5 × 4 =
     50 × 4 =
     52 × 4 =

BRAIN TEASER

Write the answers into this cross-number puzzle.

Across				**Down**			
1	9x4	**9**	4x5	**1**	8x4	**7**	6x3
3	5x9	**10**	7x3	**2**	4x3	**8**	9x9
4	8x4	**12**	8x6	**3**	7x6	**9**	4x6
5	1x2	**13**	3x3	**4**	5x7	**10**	7x4
7	5x3	**14**	8x7	**6**	10x5	**11**	4x4

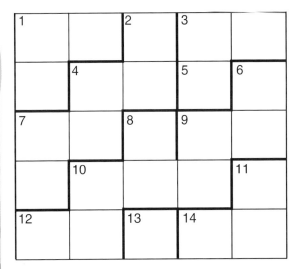

It's a mathematical fact that I'm much quicker at my multiplication facts than Mel! This game is fun and I learn my multiplication facts. Write each of the facts for all the times tables on a separate card. Shuffle the cards and lay them in a pile face up. Set a timer and see how many facts you can answer correctly in one minute. Check each answer as you go along. Keep a record of the number you answer and then after a few days see if you can beat your best score. That's how I beat my sister's score!

4x6   5x7

Challenge

23

Division is the inverse or opposite of multiplication.

This is very useful, because if you know your tables it can help you to divide numbers.

$$8 \times 3 = 24$$

$$24 \div 3 = 8$$

$$24 \div 8 = 3$$

Sometimes divisions aren't exact and leave remainders.

$$23 \div 4 = 5 \text{ remainder } 3$$

There are several ways of writing a division:

$$24 \div 3$$

$$\frac{24}{3}$$

$$3\overline{)24}$$

All these mean 24 divided by 3.

DIVIDE AND CONQUER

Q1 Write the missing numbers in each of these.

a $3 \times \boxed{} = 27$

b $\boxed{} \div 7 = 5$

c $5 \times \boxed{} = 15$

d $18 \div \boxed{} = 3$

e $\boxed{} \times 6 = 24$

f $\boxed{} \div 7 = 8$

g $9 \times \boxed{} = 63$

h $28 \div 4 = \boxed{}$

i $\boxed{} \div 8 = 6$

Q2 Answer these.

a $4\overline{)16} = \boxed{}$

b $12 \div 4 = \boxed{}$

c $\dfrac{21}{3} = \boxed{}$

d $6\overline{)42} = \boxed{}$

e $32 \div 8 = \boxed{}$

f $\dfrac{30}{5} = \boxed{}$

Q3 Write the answers.

a 15 sweets are shared equally between two people. How many sweets does each person get and how many are left over? _____

b What is the remainder when 11 is divided by 3? _____

c 50 flowers are made into bunches using 7 flowers in each bunch. How many flowers will be left over? _____

d How many times will 8 go into 26? _____

e Egg boxes hold 6 eggs. How many full boxes can be filled with 57 eggs? _____

f Class 4S are going on a trip. There has to be one adult for every 5 children. There are 48 children in total. How many adults will they need? _____

g Four children have to share 39 stickers fairly between them. How many stickers will each child get? _____

KEY DATA

If divisions aren't exact and leave a remainder, you need to make a decision whether to round up or round down for division problems.

Examples:

Rounding up: A box holds 6 bulbs. How many boxes are needed for 16 bulbs? Answer: 3 boxes are needed (one will have four bulbs in it).

Rounding down: 16 books are shared equally between 6 people. How many will each get? Answer: 2 books each, with 4 left over.

Shhhh! Don't tell Sam I'm using his multiplication fact game to learn division facts. All you have to do is write each of the division facts on 100 separate cards and write the answers on the back of them. Shuffle them (quietly!) and lay them in a pile face up. Set a timer and see how many facts you can answer correctly in one minute. Check each answer as you go along. Keep a record of the number you answer and then after a few days see if you can beat your best score. I will see if I can beat Sam!

Challenge

BRAIN TEASER

Find a route home. You can only travel on roads that can be divided exactly by 7 or 9.

Colour the route you take.

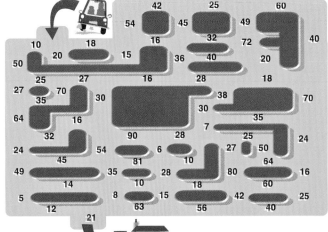

STUPENDOUS PROBLEM-SOLVING

Read word problems carefully to work out the calculations that are needed. Always follow these four easy steps:

Step 1 Read the problem.

Try to picture the problem and imagine going through it in real-life.

Step 2 Sort out the calculations.

You might need to add, subtract, multiply or divide. Sometimes more than one calculation is needed.

Step 3 Answer the calculations.

Work out the answers carefully.

Step 4 Answer the problem.

Look back at the question – what is it asking?

Q1 Read these word problems carefully and write the answer. Some questions have more than one calculation.

a My Dad is 30 years older than me, and his dad (my Grandad) is 30 years older than him. My Grandad is 68, how old am I? _____

b A bus left the station with 33 passengers. At the next bus stop 7 people got off and 4 people got on. How many people are on the bus now? _____

c I have planted 6 tomato plants. It says on the packet that each plant will have about 40 tomatoes. Approximately how many tomatoes will I have in total? _____

d There will be 11 people at Gita's party. There need to be enough sausages for everyone to have three each. The sausages are in packs of 8. How many packs does she need to buy? _____

Q2 **Look at these prices and then answer the questions.**

a Kate is saving £10 each week. How many weeks will it take for her to save enough money to buy the hi-fi?

b In a sale there is £19 off the price of the TV. What will the TV cost in the sale?

c What is the total cost of the radio and hi-fi?

d Which is cheapest: • the TV with built in video

• buying a separate TV and video player?

e Mr Piper has £200. How much more does he need to buy the hi-fi and the TV with built in video?

f Mrs Key has three grandchildren. She is going to buy each of them a radio. How much change will she have from £100?

Mel is a problem I need to solve! This challenge would make her brain ache, but you'll find it no problem if you're as intelligent as me!

Use the digits 1, 2, 3 and 4 to make different numbers. You can use +, -, x or ÷ and put them in any order. For example:

12 − 4 + 3 = 11

(21 + 3) ÷ 4 = 6

I managed to make all the numbers to 20. See if you can go even further.

Challenge

BRAIN TEASER

Try these 'think of a number' problems:

1 I think of a number, then take away 15. The answer is 25.

What was my number? _____

2 I think of a number, then divide by 3. The answer is 9.

What was my number? _____

3 I think of a number, then multiply by 4. The answer is 24.

What was my number? _____

MAGNIFICENT MONEY

These are the coins and notes that we use.

There are 100 pence in £1. We use a decimal point to separate the pounds from the pence:

£3.50 = 350p

£0.72 = 72p

£1.63 = 163p

Q1 Write the total of each of these sums.

a

£1.30   £2.50

Total £

b

£5.15   £3.07

Total £

c

£8.49   £1.51

Total £

d

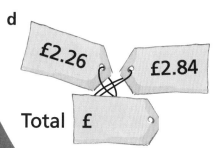

£2.26   £2.84

Total £

e

£4.68   £3.73

Total £

Q2 What is the change from £10 for each of these?

 £4.26

 84p

 £6.09

KEY DATA

To work out an amount of change, count on from the cost of the item to the amount given.

If something costs £6.88, the change from £10 is £3.12.

2p → 10p → £3.00

£6.88 £6.90 £7.00 £10

a £4.26 →
change
from £10

_____

b 84p →
change
from £10

_____

c £6.09 →
change
from £10

_____

Q3 Join pairs of prices that total £10

£2.99

£3.82

£5.50

£5.25

£1.37

£7.01

£4.50

£4.75

£9.58

£8.63

£0.42

£6.18

My name spells more
than Mel!

S = 19p   M = 13p
A = 1p   E = 5p
M = 13p   L = 12p
Total: 33p   Total: 30p

Can you see how we worked it out? A is
worth 1p, B is 2p, C is 3p and so on.

What is your name worth? Can you find any
names that are worth 50p? (Clue: look
at the author of this book!) What
is the most expensive name you can
think of? My cousin Victoria is
worth 97p!

Challenge

BRAIN TEASER

Use six coins to make these different
amounts.

1 £4.91

2 £1.87

3 £3.19

4 £2.68

29

Information can be shown in lots of different ways, using graphs, charts, tables and diagrams. You must read all the different parts carefully to understand each type.

1 Read the title. What is the graph about?

2 Look at the axis labels. These will explain the horizontal and vertical lines

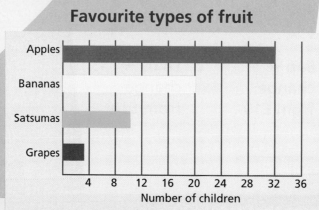

Favourite types of fruit

3 Work out the scale. Do the numbers go up in 1s, 2s, 4s, 5s, 10s …?

4 Compare the bars. Read them across and down to work out the amounts.

GLORIOUS GRAPHS

Q1 This graph shows the number of videos rented out by a shop in a week. Use the graph to answer these questions.

a How many videos were rented out on Tuesday? _____

b On which day were 47 videos rented out? _____

c How many more videos were rented out on Friday than on Monday? _____

d On which day were 15 more videos rented out than on Wednesday? _____

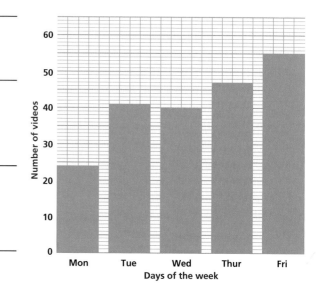

Q2 **This pictogram shows a record of the number of birds visiting a bird table.**

8-9am	🐦🐦🐦🐦
9-10am	🐦🐦🐦🐦
10-11am	🐦🐦🐦
11-12noon	🐦🐦🐦🐦
12-1pm	🐦🐦🐦🐦🐦
1-2pm	🐦🐦🐦🐦🐦🐦
2-3pm	🐦🐦
3-4pm	

KEY: 🐦 represents 5 birds

🐦🐦 represents between 5 and 10 birds

a How many birds were seen on the bird table between 11.00am and 12.00 noon? _____

b During which period were 17 birds seen on the bird table? _____

c Approximately how many birds were seen between 12.00 and 1.00pm? _____

d Thirteen birds were seen on the bird table between 3.00 and 4.00pm. Complete the chart to show this number.

e During which periods were 20 or more birds seen? _____

f Were more birds seen in the afternoon or in the morning? _____

KEY DATA

Pictograms are graphs made up from pictures. The important thing is to find out what each small picture stands for. Look at the key. For example, for this pictogram, one picture stands for 5 birds. It means that some answers will be approximate. Half a bird could be any number less than 5.

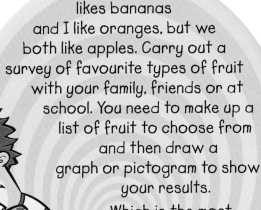

Mel likes bananas and I like oranges, but we both like apples. Carry out a survey of favourite types of fruit with your family, friends or at school. You need to make up a list of fruit to choose from and then draw a graph or pictogram to show your results.

Which is the most popular type? Which is the least popular?

Challenge

BRAIN TEASER

This tree diagram sorts numbers.

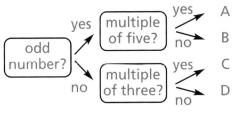

Into which box would these numbers be sorted?

1 17 → ☐   **2** 45 → ☐

3 40 → ☐   **4** 24 → ☐

Write another example for each box.

A → ☐   B → ☐   C → ☐   D → ☐

MEASUREMENT MADNESS

Try to learn these different units of measurement.

Length
1 centimetre (cm) = 10 millimetres (mm)
1 metre (m) = 100 centimetres (cm)
1 kilometre (km) = 1000 metres (m)

Weight
1 kilogram (kg) = 1000 grams (g)

Capacity
1 litre (l) = 1000 millilitres (ml)

You need to be able to read fractions of amounts. Try to learn halves, quarters and tenths of different amounts.

For example:

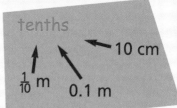

halves — $\frac{1}{2}$ m — 0.5 m — 50 cm

quarters — $\frac{1}{4}$ m — 0.25 m — 25 cm

tenths — $\frac{1}{10}$ m — 0.1 m — 10 cm

Q1 Use a ruler to measure the distances.

a Who is 40mm from A? _____

b Who is 3.5cm from D? _____

c Who is $2\frac{1}{2}$ cm from C? _____

d Who is 35mm from B? _____

e Who is 20mm from E? _____

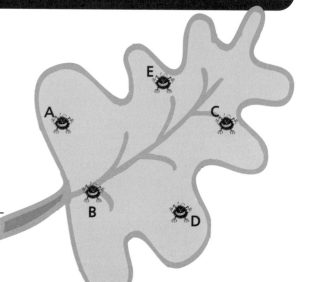

Q2 Write the measures shown.

a

b

c

_____ _____ _____

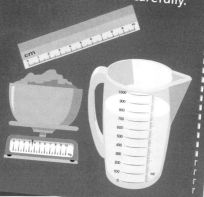

KEY DATA

When you measure, make sure you read the scale carefully.

Q3 Write the weights of these four people.

a

b

c

d

_____ _____ _____ _____

This is a good 'estimating weights' game to play with someone. I like playing it with Sam, because he just makes wild guesses, so I usually win! You need some weighing scales and lots of different items to weigh - books, tins, boxes, shoes ... that sort of thing. The first player holds an item and makes a good estimate of its weight. The second player then says 'higher' if they think the real weight is higher than the estimate, or 'lower' if they think it is lower. Check by weighing and whoever is correct wins a point. Take turns to be the estimator. First to 5 points is the winner.

Challenge

BRAIN TEASER

Perimeter = 10 cm

Area = 6 square centimetres

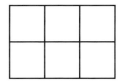

The perimeter is the distance all around the edge of a shape.

The area is the space a shape takes up.

What is the area and perimeter of this shape?

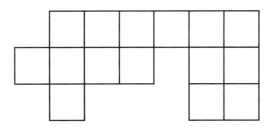

Perimeter = _____ cm

Area = _____ square cm

To make it simple to read the time with any type of clock, read the hour first and then the minutes past the hour.

three forty-two

42 minutes past 3

nine seventeen

17 minutes past 9

IT'S ABOUT TIME!

Q1 These are the start and finish times for three television programmes. Complete the missing times.

a START

10:05

The programme is

_____

minutes long.

FINISH

_____

b START

_____

The programme is

_____

minutes long.

FINISH

_____

c START

_____

The programme is

_____

minutes long.

FINISH

_____

Q2 Write out in words the times shown by these clocks.

a `03:28` _____

b `11:14` _____

c `01:53` _____

d `07:21` _____
_____

e `05:42` _____
_____

f `06:03` _____
_____

Q3 Use the calendar to answer these.

	JANUARY	FEBRUARY	MARCH	APRIL	MAY	JUNE	JULY	AUGUST
M	4 11 18 25	1 8 15 22	1 8 15 22 29	5 12 19 26	3 10 17 24 31	7 14 21 28	5 12 19 26	2 9 16 23 30
T	5 12 19 26	2 9 16 23	2 9 16 23 30	6 13 20 27	4 11 18 25	1 8 15 22 29	6 13 20 27	3 10 17 24 31
W	6 13 20 27	3 10 17 24	3 10 17 24 31	7 14 21 28	5 12 19 26	2 9 16 23 30	7 14 21 28	4 11 18 25
T	7 14 21 28	4 11 18 25	4 11 18 25	1 8 15 22 29	6 13 20 27	3 10 17 24	1 8 15 22 29	5 12 19 26
F	1 8 15 22 29	5 12 19 26	5 12 19 26	2 9 16 23 30	7 14 21 28	4 11 18 25	2 9 16 23 30	6 13 20 27
S	2 9 16 23 30	6 13 20 27	6 13 20 27	3 10 17 24	1 8 15 22 29	5 12 19 26	3 10 17 24 31	7 14 21 28
S	3 10 17 24 31	7 14 21 28	7 14 21 28	4 11 18 25	2 9 16 23 30	6 13 20 27	4 11 18 25	1 8 15 22 29

a A Youth Club meets on the second Thursday of each month. Circle these dates.

b The Youth Club camp runs for one week beginning on the last Friday in July. Cross out these dates.

KEY DATA
Mornings and afternoons/evenings are shown by am and pm

6:45am is in the morning

6:45pm is in the evening

Challenge

I've worked out that I'm over 4 million minutes old! It takes me about a minute to eat a packet of crisps – so I could have eaten 4 million packets of crisps in my lifetime! I wonder if I would be fed up with them?

Check my maths with a calculator. Have you been alive for over 4 million minutes?

BRAIN TEASER

A bus takes 25 minutes between each bus stop. Complete this timetable.

	Bus 1	Bus 2	Bus 3
Mill Lane	7:45am	_____	_____
The Hospital	_____	11:20am	
Green Park	_____		2:55pm

A 3-D shape is a solid shape. These are the parts of a 3-D shape:

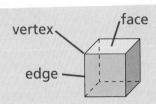

vertex
face
edge

This cube has 6 faces, 12 edges and 8 vertices.

If a 3-D shape has flat faces and straight edges it is called a <u>polyhedron</u>. These are all polyhedra:

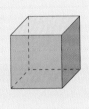 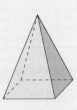 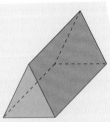

cube   cuboid   pyramid   prism

SHAPING UP IN 3-D

Q1 **Answer the questions abut 3-D shapes and find the hidden word.**

1 This shape always has two end faces the same size and shape.
2 The proper name for a box shape.
3 Pipes are usually this shape.
4 The triangle faces of this shape always meet at a point.
5 This is a perfectly round shape.
6 Six square faces make this very special shape.
7 The line where two faces meet.
8 This is a better name for a corner or point.
9 One flat side of a 3-D shape.

Hidden word:

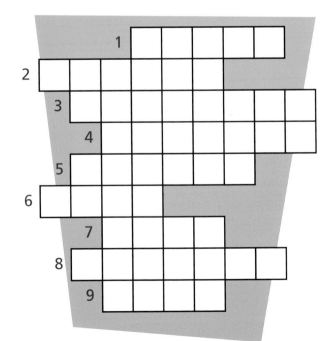

_____

Q2 Join the labels to the correct 3-D shapes in this picture.

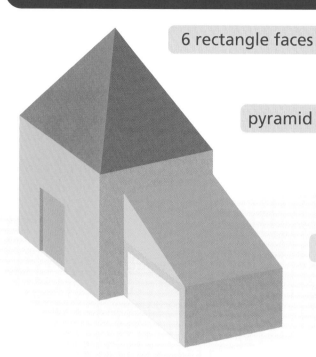

6 rectangle faces

cuboid

cube

pyramid

12 equal length edges

2 triangle faces

prism

5 vertices

KEY DATA

Prisms have two matching end faces and rectangle sides.

If you cut a slice down a prism it will always be the same size and shape as each end.

Cuboids and cubes are special prisms.

I enjoy drawing cubes, cuboids and prisms. I've got a clever, easy method and I haven't told Sam how I do it.

Try drawing these:

Cuboid. Draw two overlapping squares. Join the four corners.
Triangular prism. Draw two overlapping triangles. Join the three corners.

Practise this for other prisms.

Challenge

BRAIN TEASER

3-D shapes pass through each of these holes. The shadow of each shape can be seen.

Name the four shapes.

1 ○ ▲ _____

2 ▲ ■ _____

3 ○ ■ _____

4 □ ■ _____

SMASHING 2-D SHAPES

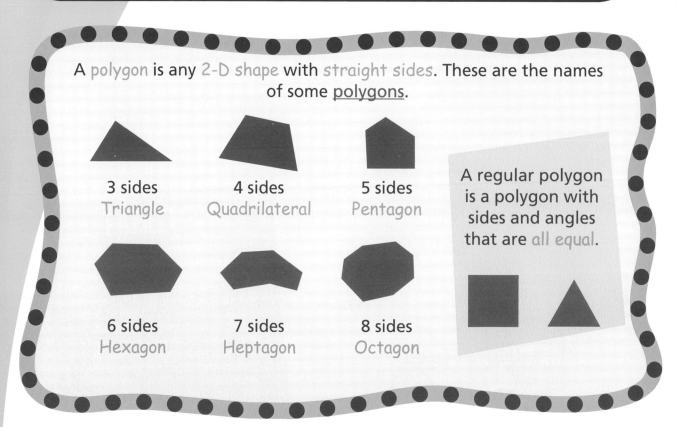

A polygon is any 2-D shape with straight sides. These are the names of some <u>polygons</u>.

3 sides
Triangle

4 sides
Quadrilateral

5 sides
Pentagon

6 sides
Hexagon

7 sides
Heptagon

8 sides
Octagon

A regular polygon is a polygon with sides and angles that are all equal.

Q1 Sort these shapes. Draw them in the correct part of the Venn diagram.

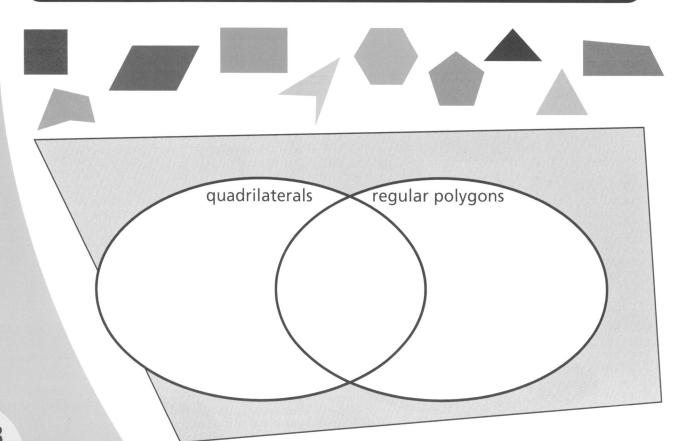

quadrilaterals   regular polygons

Q2 Each large shape is made from two smaller shapes. Complete the sentence for each shape

a This _____ is made with two _____.

b This _____ is made with two _____.

c This _____ is made with two _____.

d This _____ is made with two _____.

Q3 Look carefully at this hexagon. How many different shapes can you see?

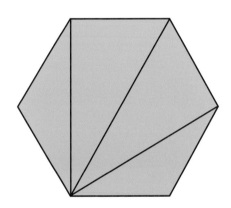

a ____ triangles

b ____ quadrilaterals

c ____ pentagons

KEY DATA

Some shapes have more than one name.

For example a rectangle is a quadrilateral with 4 right angles. A square is a special rectangle, because the four sides are equal.

This is a puzzle I set for Mel and she still hasn't solved it! Start with a rectangular piece of paper. You can fold it in any way you like and then make a single straight cut with scissors.

When you unfold it, you need to make a hexagon.

If you manage that, try making other polygons by folding and making a single cut.

Challenge

BRAIN TEASER

Copy each shape so it is exactly the same, but upside down.

The first one has been done for you.

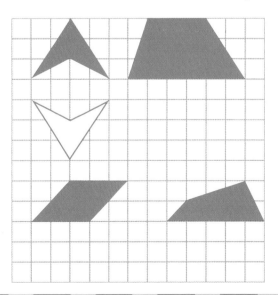

A shape is symmetrical if both sides are exactly the same when a <u>mirror</u> <u>line</u> is drawn.

Reflected shape

Shape with one <u>line</u> of <u>symmetry</u>.

Shape with two lines of symmetry.

SPECTACULAR SYMMETRY

Q1 Tick the symmetrical badges. Draw in the lines of symmetry.

a ☐

b ☐

c ☐

d ☐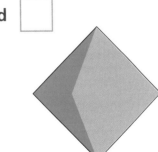

e ☐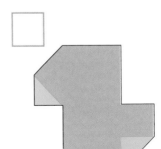

f ☐

Q2 Draw lines of symmetry on each shape.

a 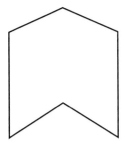 b  c  d

Q3 Draw the reflection of each shape.

a 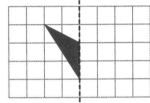 b 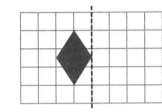 c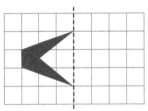

d 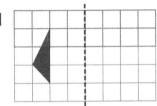 e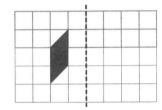

KEY DATA

Sketching the reflection of a shape can be quite tricky. It helps if the shape is drawn on a grid. Count the number of squares from a corner of the shape to the mirror line, and the reflected corner will be the same number of squares from the other side of the mirror line.

I'm feeling very pleased with myself, because I've designed my own symmetrical logo. Can you see the letters M E L in the design?

Look in magazines and around the house for different logos and signs. Are any of them symmetrical? Make up your own symmetrical logo - you can use colour or make it a line drawing.

Challenge

BRAIN TEASER

Which of these is a reflection of the first pattern. Circle the correct tile.

41

Angles are measured in degrees (°).

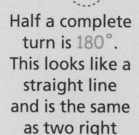

A complete turn is 360° which is the same as four right angles.

Half a complete turn is 180°. This looks like a straight line and is the same as two right angles.

A quarter turn is 90°, also called a right angle.

Half a right-angle is 45°.

North
NW   NE
West   East
SW   SE
South

There are eight compass directions: North, North-east, East, South-east, South, South-west West, North-west

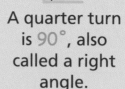

clockwise

anticlockwise

DAFT DIRECTION AND ANGLES

Q1 Look at the angles and answer these.

a Which is the smallest angle? _____

b What is the size of angle X? _____

c Which angle is 45°? _____

d Which angle is 60°? _____

e Which angle is 30°? _____

f What is the size of angle Z? _____

g Which angle is a right angle? _____

Q2 These compass directions are painted on the school playground. Mel and Sam take turns to stand in the middle and follow these instructions. Write the direction they will be facing each time.

a Sam faces North and then turns 180° clockwise.
Which direction is he now facing? _____

b Mel faces East and then turns 90° anticlockwise.
Which direction is she now facing? _____

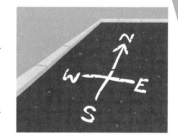

c Sam faces South and turns 45° clockwise.
Which direction is he now facing? _____

Q3 True or False? Write true or false beside each of these statements.

a If you make a 360° turn you would
end up facing the same way as
you started. _____

b A right angle is 60°. _____

c Mel and Sam both faced North.
Mel turned 180° clockwise and
Mel turned 180° anticlockwise.
Now they are both facing South. _____

KEY DATA

If you are comparing the size of different angles, remember that the sharper the point, the smaller the angle. 180°, 90° and 45° are easy to recognise, so use these to work out others. Is the angle greater or smaller than 90°? 45°?

Another important angle is 60°. These are the angles of the corners of an equilateral triangle.

I'm sending Mel on a mystery tour! With any luck, she won't find her way back!

Set up a mystery course of your own. Mark a starting point with an object, such as a chair, and use paces and turns to give someone directions to follow, to get back to the starting point.
For example: START → 4 paces forward → 90° turn clockwise → 3 paces forward → 90° turn clockwise → 1 pace forward → 90° clockwise → 5 paces forward → 90° anticlockwise → 3 paces forward → 90° anticlockwise → 2 paces forward → FINISH

Challenge

BRAIN TEASER

Write all the different routes to get from the house to the shop. You can only travel north-east or south-east. One route has been written to start you off.

SE 1 square

NE 2 squares

SE 1 square

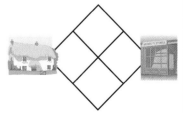

TEST PRACTICE

1 Write the missing numbers.

3845 = 3000 + ☐ + ☐ + 5

2 Circle the correct weight of the parcel.

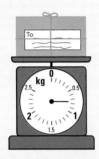

250g   750g   500g   700g

3 150 – 70 = ☐

4 Write the missing numbers in this sequence.

47   41   ☐   29   ☐   ☐   11

5 Name this shape.

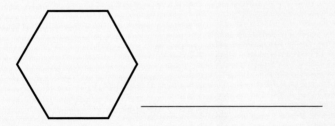

_____

6 Draw the lines of symmetry on the shape.

7   Write the missing number.

☐ × 4 = 28

MENU

Rice   £2.30

Chow Mein   £2.15

Sweet and Sour Chicken   £3.42

Prawn Crackers   84p

8   Which 5 coins would you need to buy some prawn crackers?

9   What change will there be from £10 for Sweet and Sour Chicken and Rice?

_____

10 Complete these fractions.

$$\frac{2}{3} = \frac{\square}{6} = \frac{8}{\square}$$

11 A bus leaves a bus station and arrives at the hospital at 11.25am. The journey took 35 minutes. What time did the bus leave the bus station?

_____

score

12 Draw the reflection of this shape.

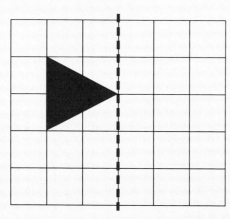

13 Write the missing number.

2030 ÷ ☐ = 203

14 Answer this.

```
   394
+   68
───────

───────
```

15 A jug holds 2.5 litres. A cup holds 250ml. How many cupfuls are needed to fill the jug?

16 Join these shapes with a line to the correct part of this Carroll Diagram.

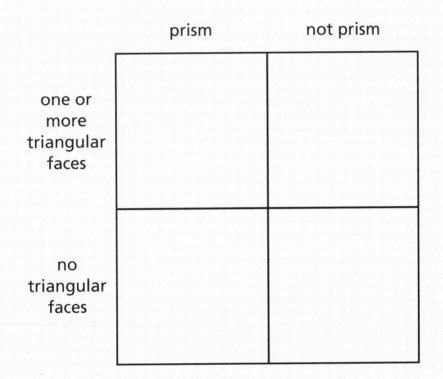

prism   not prism

one or more triangular faces

no triangular faces

17 46 people are going on a trip. They use minibuses that each hold 10 people. How many minibuses will they need for their trip?

_____

score

18 A cake costs 82p.

How many can you buy for £4?

_____

19 What change would you get?

_____

20 Shade 1/5 of this grid.

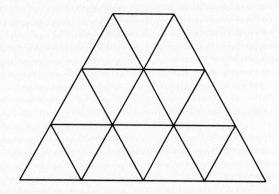

21 Write these numbers in the correct places.

147   213   192

182 > ⬚ < ⬚ < 205 < ⬚

22 What is the difference between 37 and 94?

_____

23 What is the area and perimeter of this shape?

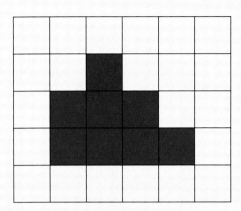

Area = ☐ cm²

Perimeter = ☐ cm

24 Answer this.

34 × 4 = ☐

25 Gemma took 2 minutes and 24 seconds to complete a race. How many seconds is this?

_____

ANSWERS

Pages 4–5

Q1
a 3206   **b** 5741   **c** 8190
d 9919   **e** 4052   **f** 7611

Q2
a 4152 = 4000 + 100 + 50 + 2
b 7338 = 7000 + 300 + 30 + 8
c 9624 = 9000 + 600 + 20 + 4
d 8513 = 8000 + 500 + 10 + 3
e 2299 = 2000 + 200 + 90 + 9
f 1687 = 1000 + 600 + 80 + 7

Q3
a 34 — x 10 → 340 / x100 → 3400
b 70 — x 10 → 700 / x100 → 7000
c 56 — x 10 → 560 / x100 → 5600
d 92 — x 10 → 920 / x100 → 9200

Brain Teaser

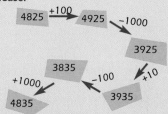

4825 → +100 → 4925 → −1000 → 3925 → +10 → 3935 → −100 → 3835 → +1000 → 4835

Pages 6–7

Q1

smallest	75
	517
	570
	705
	715
	5110
	5771
	5775
largest	7005

Q2
a <   **d** <   **g** >   **j** >
b >   **e** >   **h** >   **k** <
c <   **f** >   **i** <   **l** >

Q3
a 56   57   61   59   60   58
b 3131   3133   3132   3134   3135   3136
c 988   989   990   993   992   991
d 420   410   430   440   450   460
e 6400   6500   6700   6600   6800   6900

Brain Teaser

There are many possible answers, check child's answer.

Pages 8–9

Q1

	Nearest 10	Nearest 100
a	120	100
b	400	400
c	580	600
d	320	300
e	650	700
f	250	200

Q2 **a** £1   **b** £7   **c** £5   **d** £9

Q3 **a** 10   **b** 30   **c** 50   **d** 80

Q4 **a** 340   **b** 760   **c** 300   **d** 165

Brain Teaser

1 £2.30   **2** £2.20   **3** £2.00

Pages 10–11

Q1
a 28, 34, 40   **d** 525, 500, 475
b 18, 13, 8   **e** 299, 297, 295
c 450, 470, 490

Q2
a 20, 26   **b** 650, 500
c 20, 28   **d** 56, 21

Q3

a

−8	−6	−4	−2	0	−2	−4

b

−11	−9	−7	−5	−3	−1	1

c

−15	−10	−5	0	5	10	15

d

25	15	5	−5	−15	−25	−35

Brain Teaser

10	11	12	13	14	15	16	17	18	19
9	44	45	46	47	48	49	50	51	20
8	43	70	71	72	73	74	75	52	21
7	42	69	88	89	90	91	76	53	22
6	41	68	87	98	99	92	77	54	23
5	40	67	86	97	100	93	78	55	24
4	39	66	85	96	95	94	79	56	25
3	38	65	84	83	82	81	80	57	26
3	37	64	63	62	61	60	59	58	27
1	36	35	34	33	32	31	30	29	28

Pages 12–13

Q1 **a** $\frac{2}{3}$ **b** $\frac{5}{6}$ **c** $\frac{7}{8}$ **d** $\frac{1}{2}$
e $\frac{5}{6}$ **f** $\frac{4}{4}$

Q2 **a** any one part shaded
b any two parts shaded
c any five parts shaded

Q3

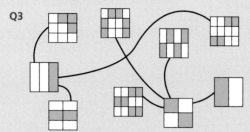

Brain Teaser
$\frac{1}{4}$ $\frac{1}{2}$ $\frac{3}{5}$ $\frac{7}{10}$ $\frac{3}{4}$ $\frac{4}{5}$

Pages 14–15

Q1	**a** 8	**e** 7	**i** 3
	b 5	**f** 4	**j** 4
	c 3	**g** 3	
	d 11	**h** 2	

Q2 **a** 6   **b** 8   **c** 12   **d** 4

Q3 **a** 60p   **b** 3   **c** 6
d 3   **e** $\frac{1}{2}$

Brain Teaser

1  = $\frac{3}{4}$ 2 = $\frac{1}{3}$

3 = $\frac{1}{4}$

Pages 16–17

Q1	**a** 96	**h** 38
	b 52	**i** 91
	c 93	**j** 73
	d 77	**k** 77
	e 82	**l** 36
	f 96	**m** 71
	g 93	**n** 91

Q2

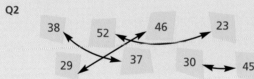

Q3	**a** £95	**e** £64
	b £41	**f** £78
	c £66	**g** £136
	d £84	

Brain Teaser

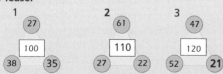

Pages 18–19

Q1	**a** 44	**f** 37
	b 33	**g** 57
	c 48	**h** 17
	d 15	**i** 54
	e 9	**j** 12

Q2	**a** 19	**d** 45
	b 39	**e** 38
	c 18	**f** 23

Q3	**a** 7 years	**e** 26 years old
	b 57 years	**f** Dad and Gran
	c 19 years	**g** 28 years
	d 29 years	

Brain Teaser

1 A and E   2 33
3 C   4 True

Pages 20–21

Q1 **a** 384   **b** 317   **c** 501   **d** 591

Q2 **a** 138   **b** 383   **c** 169   **d** 171

Q3

```
a      3  8  4      c      7  6  1
    +     4  7          –     8  8
    ─────────          ────────
       4  3  1             6  7  3

b      5  1  9      d      6  4  2
    +     9  2          –     5  3
    ─────────          ────────
       6  1  1             5  8  9
```

Q4 **a** 564   **b** 567

Brain Teaser

```
     3  1              3  1
     6  2              2  6
  +     2  4        +     2  4
  ─────────        ─────────
     1  1  7              8  1
```

Pages 22–23

Q1
	a	**b**	**c**
	$7 \times 2 = 14$	$8 \times 3 = 24$	$7 \times 9 = 63$
	$4 \times 4 = 16$	$9 \times 2 = 18$	$5 \times 8 = 40$
	$5 \times 9 = 45$	$5 \times 5 = 25$	$6 \times 3 = 18$
	$3 \times 8 = 24$	$6 \times 7 = 42$	$4 \times 7 = 28$
	$6 \times 6 = 36$	$10 \times 4 = 40$	$9 \times 8 = 72$
	$4 \times 3 = 12$	$4 \times 9 = 36$	$5 \times 6 = 30$
	$2 \times 10 = 20$	$3 \times 7 = 21$	$6 \times 8 = 48$
	$5 \times 6 = 30$	$2 \times 8 = 16$	$9 \times 9 = 81$

Q2

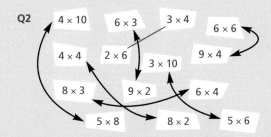

Q3
a $3 \times 5 = 15$
   $30 \times 5 = 150$
b $7 \times 9 = 63$
   $70 \times 9 = 630$
c $8 \times 4 = 32$
   $80 \times 4 = 320$
d $5 \times 4 = 20$
   $50 \times 4 = 200$
   $52 \times 4 = 208$

Brain Teaser

¹3	6	²1	³4	5
2	⁴3	2	⁵2	⁶5
⁷1	5	⁸9	⁹2	0
8	¹⁰2	1	4	¹¹1
¹²4	8	¹³9	¹⁴5	6

Pages 24–25
Q1 a 9   d 6   g 7
     b 35   e 4   h 7
     c 3   f 56   i 48

Q2 a 4   b 3   c 7
     d 7   e 4   f 6

Q3 a 7 sweets each and 1 left over
     b 2
     c 1
     d 3
     e 9
     f 10
     g 9

Brain Teaser
There is more than one answer, check child's route.

Pages 26–27
Q1 a 8 years old   b 30
     c 240   d 5 packs

Q2 a 9 weeks
     b £66
     c £112
     d Neither, they are the same price.
     e £36
     f £16

Brain Teaser
1 40   2 27   3 6

Pages 28–29
Q1 a £3.80   d £5.10
     b £8.22   e £8.41
     c £10

Q2 a £5.74   b £9.16   c £3.91

Q3

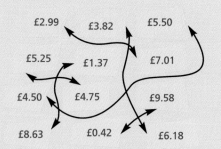

Brain Teaser
1 £2, £2, 50p, 20p, 20p, 1p coins
2 £1, 50p, 20p, 10p, 5p, 2p coins
3 £2, £1, 10p, 5p, 2p, 2p, coins
4 £2, 50p, 10p, 5p, 2p, 1p, coins

Pages 30–31
Q1 a 1   b Thursday   c 31
     d Friday

Q2 a 20
     b 9–10am
     c between 21 and 24 birds
     d
     e 8–9am, 11–12noon, 12–1pm, 1–2pm
     f afternoon

Brain Teaser
1 B   2 A   3 D   4 C

Pages 32–33
Q1 a D   b E   c D   d E
     e C

Q2 a 240ml   b 380ml   c 110ml

Q3 a 30kg   b 85kg   c 50kg   d 75kg

Brain Teaser
Perimeter = 24cm   Area = 15cm²

Pages 34–35
Q1 a 10.05 → 40 minutes → 10.45
     b 4.20 → 55 minutes → 5.15
     c 7.55 → 45minutes → 8.40

Q2 a 28 minutes past 3 or three twenty-eight
     b 14 minutes past 11 or eleven fourteen
     c 53 minutes past 1 or one fifty-three
     d 21 minutes past 7 or seven twenty-one
     e 42 minutes past 5 or five forty-two
     f 3 minutes past 6 or six zero three

Q3

	JANUARY	FEBRUARY	MARCH	APRIL
M	4 11 18 25	1 8 15 22	1 8 15 22 29	5 12 19 26
T	5 12 19 26	2 9 16 23	2 9 16 23 30	6 13 20 27
W	6 13 20 27	3 10 17 24	3 10 17 24 31	7 14 21 28
T	7 ⑭ 21 28	4 ⑪ 18 25	4 ⑪ 18 25	1 ⑧ 15 22 29
F	1 8 15 22 29	5 12 19 26	5 12 19 26	2 9 16 23 30
S	2 9 16 23 30	6 13 20 27	6 13 20 27	3 10 17 24
S	3 10 17 24 31	7 14 21 28	7 14 21 28	4 11 18 25

	MAY	JUNE	JULY	AUGUST
M	3 10 17 24 31	7 14 21 28	5 12 19 26	2 9 16 23 30
T	4 11 18 25	1 8 15 22 29	6 13 20 27	3 10 17 24 31
W	5 12 19 26	2 9 16 23 30	7 14 21 28	4 11 18 25
T	6 ⑬ 20 27	3 ⑩ 17 24	1 ⑧ 15 22 29	5 ⑫ 19 26
F	7 14 21 28	4 11 18 25	2 9 16 23 30	6 13 20 27
S	1 8 15 22 29	5 12 19 26	3 10 17 24 31	7 14 21 28
S	2 9 16 23 30	6 13 20 27	4 11 18 25	1 8 15 22 29

Brain Teaser

	Bus1	Bus 2	Bus 3
Mill Lane	7:45am	8:10am	8:35am
The Hospital	10:55am	11:20am	11:45am
Green Park	2:05pm	2:30pm	2:55pm

Pages 36–37
Q1

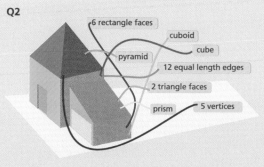

1 p r i s m
2 c u b o i d
3 c y l i n d e r
4 p y r a m i d
5 s p h e r e
6 c u b e
7 e d g e
8 v e r t e x
9 f a c e

Hidden word: polyhedra

Q2

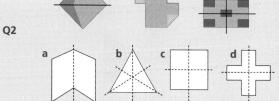

- 6 rectangle faces
- cuboid
- cube
- pyramid
- 12 equal length edges
- 2 triangle faces
- prism
- 5 vertices

Brain Teaser

1 cone   2 prism
3 cylinder   4 cuboid

Pages 38–39
Q1

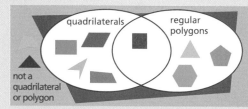

quadrilaterals   regular polygons

not a quadrilateral or polygon

Q2
a This rectangle is made with two pentagons.
b This polygon is made with two triangles.
c This pentagon is made with two quadrilaterals.
d This hexagon is made with two quadrilaterals.

Q3
a 4 triangles   b 3 quadrilaterals
c 2 pentagons

Brain Teaser

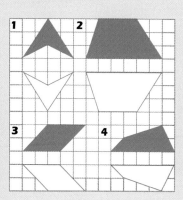

Pages 40–41
Q1

a ✓   b ✓   c ☐

d ✓   e ☐   f ✓

Q2

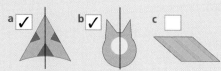

a   b   c   d

Q3

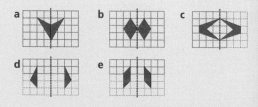

a   b   c

d   e

Brain Teaser

Pages 42–43

Q1
a v
b 90°
c y
d w
e v
f 180°
g x

Q2
a South
b North
c South West

Q3
a True
b False
c True

Brain Teaser

There are six different routes. Check child's answers.

Pages 44–45 Test Practice

1 800 + 40

2 750g

3 80

4 35, 23, 17

5 hexagon

6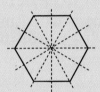

7 7

8 50p, 20p, 10p, 2p, 2p

9 £6.58

10 $\frac{2}{3} = \frac{4}{6} = \frac{8}{12}$

11 10.50 am

12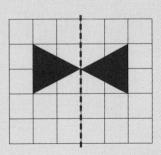

13 10

14 462

15 10 cupfuls

16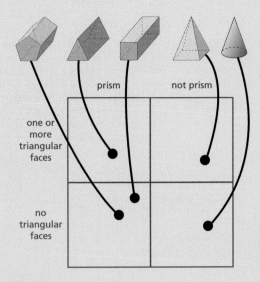

17 5

18 4

19 72p

20 Any 3 parts can be shaded.

21 182 > 147 < 192 < 205 < 213

22 57

23 Area = 8cm²

Perimeter = 14cm

24 136

25 144 seconds

REALLY USEFUL WORDS

<u>Approximate</u> An approximate answer is very close to the right answer, but not exact. 47 + 19 is approximately 50 + 20, which is 70.

<u>Capacity</u> Capacity is the amount of space in a container or the amount of liquid it will hold.

<u>Column</u> A column is a vertical line going up or down.

<u>Denominator</u> The denominator is the number below the line in a fraction. It shows how many parts a whole shape or number of items is divided into. $\frac{1}{4}$ of 12. The denominator is 4, so $\frac{1}{4}$ of 12 is 12 ÷ 4 = 3.

<u>Difference</u> The difference is the number you must count on to get from a smaller number to a bigger one. You can also work it out by subtracting the smaller one from the bigger one. The difference between 8 and 12 is 4.

<u>Digit</u> A digit is any of the ten numerals: 0, 1, 2, 3, 4, 5, 6, 7, 8 or 9. Numbers are made up from digits.

<u>Estimate</u> To estimate a number means to decide roughly how much that number is.

<u>Length</u> Length is the distance between two points or the two ends of a line.

<u>Line</u> of <u>symmetry</u> A line of symmetry is a line about which a shape is symmetrical. If the shape is folded along the line, one half fits exactly over the other half.

Mirror line A mirror line is another name for a line of symmetry and is a line about which a shape is symmetrical. If a mirror is placed on the line, the half shape and its reflection show the whole shape.

Negative numbers A number less than zero is a negative number. The minus sign (–) is used to show when a number is negative.

Polygon A polygon is a flat shape with straight sides.

Polyhedron A polyhedron is a many-sided solid shape with straight edges.

Product When two or more numbers are multiplied together, the answer is the product of those numbers. The product of 5 and 6 is 30.

Remainder If a number cannot be divided exactly by another number, it can leave a remainder or an amount left over. 14 divided by 3 is 4 with 2 as a remainder.

Weight Weight is the heaviness of an object or person. A force called gravity pulls objects down and gives them weight. We usually measure weight in kilograms (kg) which are really units for measuring mass.